To Annis

Foreword

THE SONGS in this collection are the result of what you might almost call a process of spontaneous combustion: Gladys Adshead, head of the Lower School, and George Shapiro, director of Lower School Music at the North Shore Country Day School, Winnetka, Illinois, both felt the need of fresh, new material that would appeal both musically and imaginatively, particularly among younger children; and finding none that seemed exactly to fit their requirements, they made one or two experiments at collaboration in writing songs. *The Trees Have Put Their Nightgowns On* and *Snow Feathers* were presented—casually, without comment on the authorship—among other songs which the children were learning; they were sung with such spontaneous enjoyment, and were called for so often in music classes, that the partners in the enterprise were encouraged to continue their creative work.

Gladys Adshead's lyrics found their genesis in the interests and responses of the children themselves; and George Shapiro's settings, simple, various and beautifully "singable," added flavor and character, so that small fry from the four-year-old Junior Kindergarten stage to the more capable and critical sixth-grade level responded to their appeal and took such satisfaction in them that it was not long before the entire Lower School was singing the songs both in and out of class.

Some of the songs, like *Easter Is Here* and *Here We Go to the Pumpkin Shop*, admittedly have a purely seasonal appeal limited pretty much to the younger children. But just as many slight stories and verses have a strong if transitory charm and are important for the "present mirth" they evoke, so these songs serve to highlight the minor festivals so thoroughly enjoyed by little children. *Mary's Lullaby*, on the other hand, though its timeliness is limited to the Christmas season, renews its appeal from year to year among listeners and performers of all ages, because in both theme and treatment it reflects the perennial beauty and sweetness of the Christmas festival.

In presenting these songs to a wider public than has heretofore enjoyed them, author and composer intend that they should be used not to displace, but rather to supplement the wealth of folk-songs and simple art-songs that will always form the basis of good musical experience for children. These songs have been sung and continue to be sung with genuine delight and happy remembrance by successive grades of children from the age of innocence to the adolescent years of musical sophistication. It is this fact that commends them for use in classrooms and in family circles where singing should be a joyous and memorable part of childhood.

RAMSAY DUFF

Contents

Mary's Lullaby

Tiny precious Christ Child
Nestled in the hay,
Watch the little angels
Round your manger play.
Gentle little angels
Round my little One.
Angels guard you safely,
Tiny precious Son.
I and little angels

Sing you lullaby,
Singing round your manger
That you will not cry.
Lulla, lullaby—
That you will not cry,
Rock you, precious Christ Child,
That you will not cry.
Lulla, lullaby, Lulla, lullaby.

5

MARY'S LULLABY

Ti-ny pre-cious

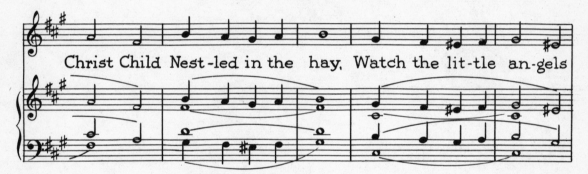

Christ Child Nest-led in the hay, Watch the lit-tle an-gels

Round your man-ger play. Gen-tle lit-tle an-gels round my lit-tle

one, An-gels guard you safe-ly Ti-ny pre-cious Son. I and lit-tle

an-gels Sing you lul-la-by,   Sing-ing round your man-ger

That you will not   cry.   Lul-la-lul-la-   by....

That you will not cry.   Rock you pre-cious Christ Child

That you will not cry.   Lul-la-lul-la-by,   Lul-la-lul-la-   by.

A LITTLE CHILD'S THANKSGIVING

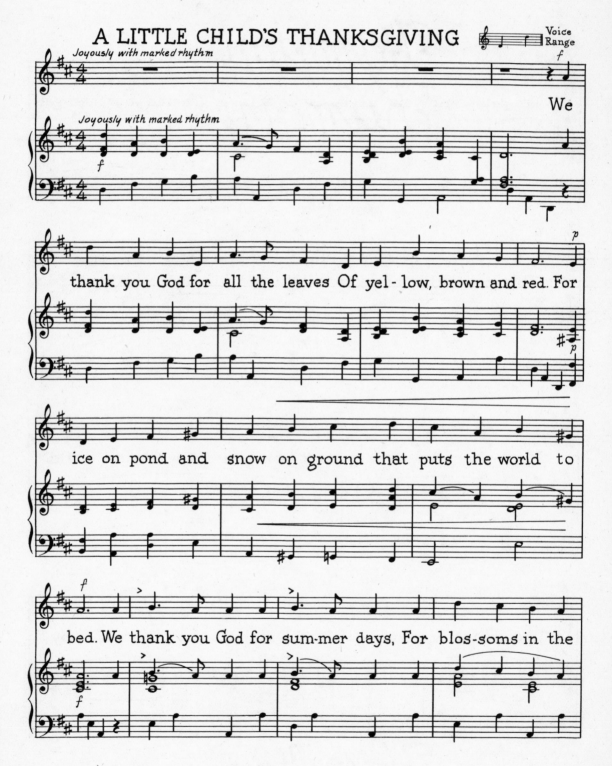

thank you God for all the leaves Of yel-low, brown and red. For

ice on pond and snow on ground that puts the world to

bed. We thank you God for sum-mer days, For blos-soms in the

spring, For lit-tle nests and lit-tle eggs and hap-py birds that sing.

SNOW FEATHERS

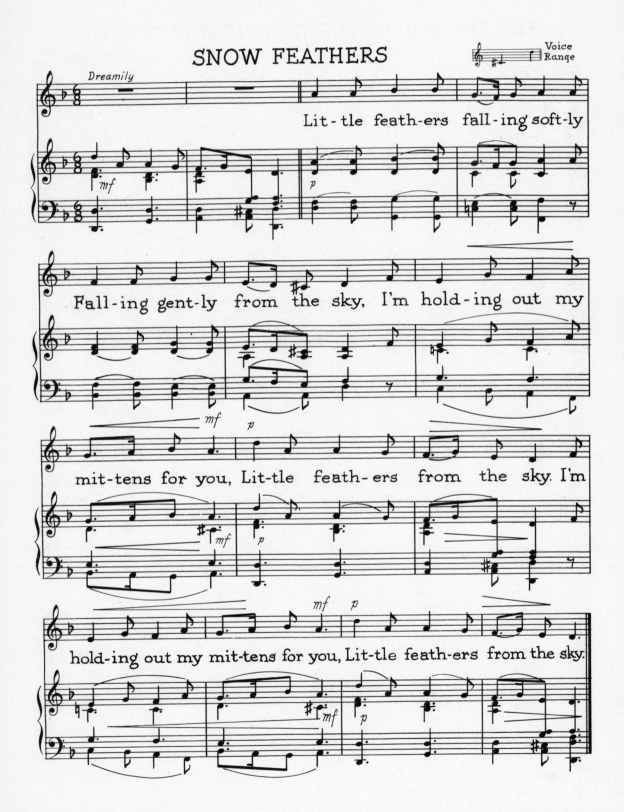

THE TREES HAVE PUT THEIR NIGHTGOWNS ON

One snow-y day "Look!" said John, "The trees have put Their night-gowns on!" Joyce said, "Look, at some-thing new! The world is spread With a

SKATING

Smoothly we go like a bird on the wing, Skat-ing, like fly-ing's a won-der-ful thing! Twist-ing and twirl-ing right o-ver the lake, In

beau-ti-ful mo -tion, glid-ing we skate. Smooth-ly we
go like a bird on the wing, Laugh-ing and shout-ing we
mer-ri-ly sing. Skat-ing and skat-ing the sun drop-ping
low, Swing-ing our skates, home now o-ver the snow.

VALENTINE'S DAY

Red can-dy hearts,

Cards with white lace, Va-len-tine greet-ings set out in each place.

Here comes the post-man Knock-ing and ring-ing.

More Val-en-tine cards I'm sure he is bring-ing. Sing, sing,

Let us sing, Let us sing, it is Va-len-tine Day, Sing, sing,

Let us sing, Let us sing it is Va-len-tine Day.

EASTER IS HERE

With spirit

1. Bounc-ing a-long comes the gay East-er Bun-ny, Hid-ing his eggs while the morn-ing is sun-ny, Twink-ling his nose and look-ing so fun-ny, Hey-ho! Hey-ho! East-er is here.

2. Red eggs, pink eggs, yel-low eggs and blue,

3. Run a-way Bun-ny, or child-ren may see,

Hid - den a - way while the morn-ing is new.
Hop down your rab-bit hole, quick as can be.

Hid - den a - way while the world's wet with dew,
Here come the child - ren shout - ing with glee.

Hey - ho! Hey - ho! East - er is here.
Hey - ho! Hey - ho! East - er is here.

OH, SPRING IS HERE

The sky is blue, the grass grows green, Pale tin-y flow-ers hide in the woods. And where the brook flows half un-seen, The wil-low cat-kins burst their hoods. Oh, spring is here! Oh, spring is here! The

pus - sy wil - lows now ap-pear   Like mid-get fur-ry

kit - tens gray   Climb-ing each slen-der wil-low spray.

a little faster

A SMALL BIRD SWINGS

Voice Range

With swinging rhythm

1. Up-on a slen-der branch of larch, branch of larch,
4. The clouds were white and ver-y soft, ver-y soft,

branch of larch, Up-on a slen-der branch of larch, I
ver-y soft, The clouds were white and ver-y soft, with

saw a small bird swing. 2. And as the breez-es swayed the trees,
lots of blue be-tween. 5. And here had come in love-li-ness,

swayed the trees, swayed the trees, And as the breez - es
love - li - ness, love - li - ness, And here had come in

swayed the trees, I heard the small bird sing. 3. The
love - li - ness, The glad and smil - ing spring 6. Then

larch tree wore her tas-sels red, Tas-sels red, tas-sels red, The
to my-self I hugged that joy, shin-ing joy, shin-ing joy, And

larch tree wore her tas-sels red, And spikes of ten-der green.
oh, I loved that shin-ing joy, That made the small bird sing.

SUNNY MORNING

What a love-ly sun-ny morn - ing, Just the time to play and sing. I'll spread my arms, Just watch me fly Like a blue-bird on the wing. I could sing and sing, so glad am

I. Tra la la, tra la la, tra la la la la. I could

sing and sing, be-neath the sky. Tra la la, tra la

la, tra la, la la.

BEES

Voice Range

Quickly and lightly

1. Bu - sy bu - sy lit - tle bees,
2. Buz buz buz buz buz buz buz.

Buz - zing round the clov - er.

Are you glad when even-ing Comes and the day is o - ver?

Buz-z-z-z-z Buz-z-z-z-z Buz-z-z-z-z Buz-z-z-z-z Buzz.

BIRDS HAVE WINGS

Birds have wings, such love-ly wings. I wish that I could fly   and

spread my wings like bees and things that sail   a-bout the

a little faster

sky.   I think I'll try, Just watch   me fly! The wind is help-ing

rit   *p*   *in time*

me,   And here am I be-neath the sky a lit-tle bird so free.

SOFTLY, SILENTLY

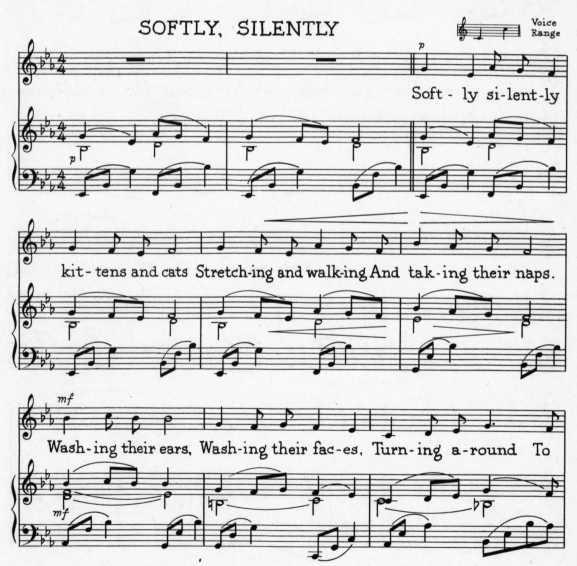

Soft - ly si - lent - ly kit - tens and cats Stretch - ing and walk - ing And tak - ing their naps.

Wash - ing their ears, Wash - ing their fac - es, Turn - ing a - round To

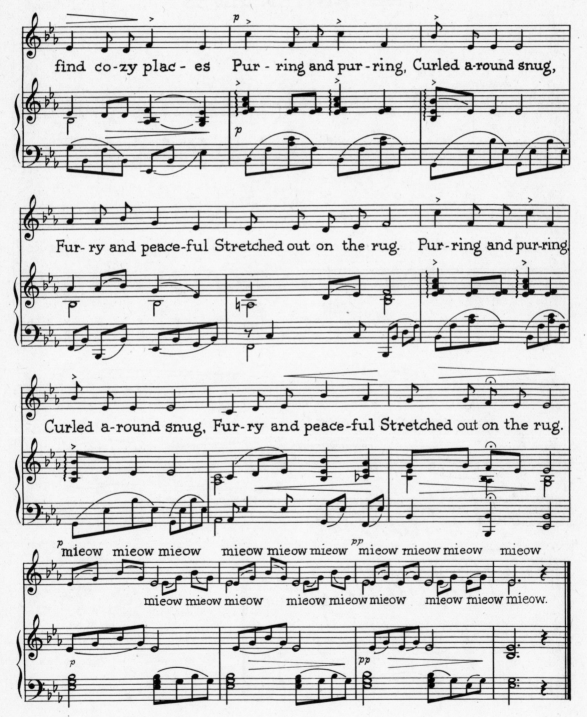

find co-zy plac - es Pur - ring and pur - ring, Curled a-round snug,

Fur-ry and peace-ful Stretched out on the rug. Pur-ring and pur-ring,

Curled a-round snug, Fur-ry and peace-ful Stretched out on the rug.

mieow mieow mieow mieow mieow mieow mieow mieow mieow mieow

mieow mieow mieow mieow mieow mieow mieow mieow mieow.

THE PAINTER ELVES

Be-fore the leaves are brown and dead The paint-er elves Roll up their sleeves, Dip-ping their brush-es In gold and red To make a splen-dor Of the leaves.

THE WIND AND I WENT DANCING

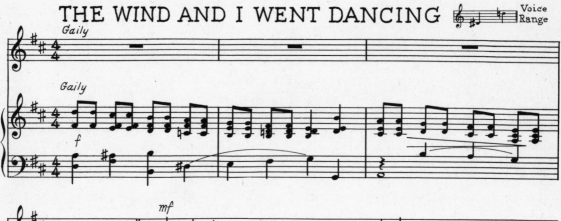

The wind and I went danc - ing One

spark - ling au - tumn day, The leaves were all a -

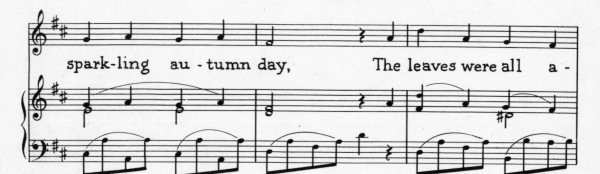

pranc - ing and looked so bright and gay. My

skirt and hair blew round my head, The leaves like feath-ers

whirled a - round, But as I tried to dance with them They

rest - ed on the ground.

HERE WE GO TO THE PUMPKIN SHOP

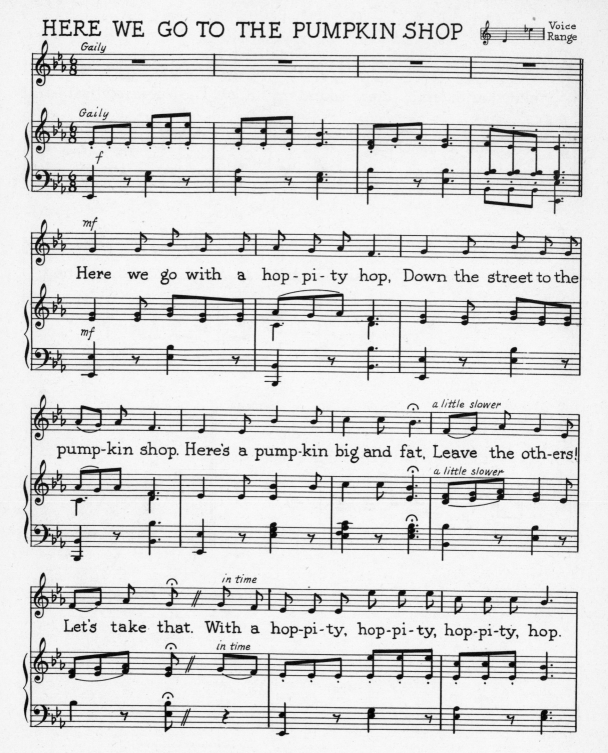

Here we go with a hop-pi-ty hop, Down the street to the pump-kin shop. Here's a pump-kin big and fat, Leave the oth-ers! Let's take that. With a hop-pi-ty, hop-pi-ty, hop-pi-ty, hop.

Hip-pi-ty-hop, hip-pi-ty-hop. Home a-gain with a hop-pi-ty-hop.

Hur-ry! Hur-ry! Cut off the top, Scoop out the seeds, Make the eyes, A

a little slower | To be spoken |

nose, a mouth. Sur-prise! Sur-prise! With a hop-pi-ty, hop-pi-ty,

Hop-pi-ty-hop. Hip-pi-ty-hop, hip-pi-ty-hop.

30818

37

HALLOWE'EN IS VERY QUEER

Witch-es, gob-lins, Owls and cats,

Lit-tle white ghost-ies. Lit-tle black bats. Fun and fro-lic And

dance with glee, When Hol-low-e'en comes For them and me

"Boo!" says the witch, "Boo, to you!" "Boo!" says the gob-lin and the

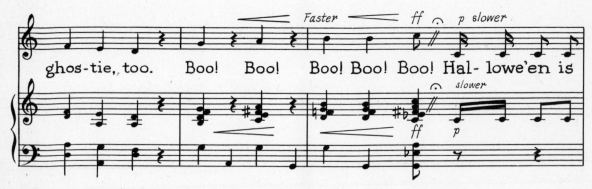

ghos-tie, too. Boo! Boo! Boo! Boo! Boo! Hal- lowe'en is

here When eve-ry-thing is ver-y queer! Boo!